THIS MONTH I'LL RESEARCH MY DREAM SCHOOL

J Patin-Sauls

TYPE SET GROW

words to live by

ISBN: 978-1-960476-00-5
FIRST EDITION JANUARY 2023

Exclusive Reader Resources

As an exclusive gift to our readers, we have created a top-secret web page where you can instantly:

- Download additional resources

- Find links to recommended programs and software

- Access special offers and promotional codes

- Take your next steps in the journey to reaching your educational goals!

This page is updated regularly, so be sure to check it out often!

www.admissionscontrol/readers

Testimonials

"I booked a session with this advisor before and he was extremely helpful! Best writing advisor I have ever met throughout my college application and transfer experience!"

Joanne K.

"Perfect and streamlined edits and suggestions. Nothing wasted. Really appreciated."

Robert G.

"Jake has put so much effort and time into helping me transform my essay into new colors. I was provided plenty of feedback, suggestions, and even sample essays to use as inspiration to fix certain weak points in my essay. "

CeeJay

"Thank you!"

Milan N.

"Thank you so much, it's very helpful with really insightful suggestions!"

Nora W.

"He has a true gift - he can propose a few subtle changes or rearrange sentences which then bring the essay to life."

Marsha A.

Testimonials

"Johnathan Patin-Sauls provided thorough and helpful feedback. He reviewed my essays and responded very quicky."

Matthew T.

"Professor Jake is the real deal...he has consistently come up with very useful insights and comments. I very much appreciated his insights, i.e. telling it Like it is, the good and the bad...went above and beyond by giving us samples as well. Highly recommended. Thank you for going that extra mile to make this work for us."

John S.

Great review. Using Johnathan again for another essay.

Emanuel C.

"Very actionable feedback. I'm very glad I chose this consultant."

Rose M.

"Exactly what I needed to hear. I value the information and will be making the necessary changes/additions."

Cullen C.

I told you my story with just words but you understood the story behind those words very well. How did you understand the story so well? I appreciate you. Thank you very much.

Alta R.

This journal belongs to:

_____

Future student at:

_____

YOU ARE THE HERO, AND THIS IS YOUR
STORY.

KNOW IT
THAT YOU MAY GROW INTO YOUR GIFTS.

MASTER IT
AS THE ONLY BIRTHRIGHT BEFITTING THE
TRUE HEIR OF A STORYTELLING PEOPLE.

TELL IT CLEARLY
THAT IT MAY BE HEARD BY THE MENTORS,
SUNG BY THE BARDS, AND WONDERED AT
BY THOSE WIDE-EYED YOUTH WHO WILL
SEE IN YOU THEIR COVERT DREAMS OF
DARING AND WANDER.

-J PATIN-SAULS

AN ADMISSIONS CONTROL

STUDENT GUIDE

TO GETTING INTO COLLEGE

THIS MONTH I'LL RESEARCH MY DREAM SCHOOL

DAILY GOALS, PROMPTS, AND TO-DO LISTS

Rocket Fuel for Your College Admissions Journey

From the Top-Rated
Educational Consultant

J Patin-Sauls

How to Use this Book
(and prepare to *crush* your college apps)

If you're reading this, chances are you're probably freaking out a little about your college applications. You're a smart person, so you've read all the statistics and the story of that one kid who built a nuclear reactor in his garage but still got rejected from MIT, and you're thinking: *okay, so I've got no chance, right?*

And yeah, the statistics don't lie (well, except when they do) but you should know that the vast majority of those rejected students are qualified for admission. So what gives? And how do you avoid ending up among their ranks?

While working one-on-one with thousands of successful students I've isolated the traits, skills, experiences, and goals these students exhibit in their applications. Do they have good grades? Sure. Exceptional extracurriculars? Sometimes. But they're always diligent, novel storytellers, who do lots of organized research.

In fact, I've found that - all other things being equal - students who spend the equivalent of one weekend (~16 active hours) visiting or seriously researching their dream school online are 3x more likely to rate themselves extremely happy at the school they eventually attend - *whether it's the same one or not* - when we strategize their graduate school applications four years later. This book was created with that number in mind: 30 activities meant to be completed, on average, in about a half-hour daily over the course of one month.

And I can't stress the importance of this research enough, post-Covid, when so many admissions officers have confided to me that they're actively seeking students who exhibit a deep knowledge of the school. The reason? Large numbers of students accepted when campuses were closed to visitors have now proven to be a "poor fit" in ways that tours would have traditionally hinted at ahead of time.

Because travel is still difficult for so many of us, it's unfortunately impossible for everyone to visit every school they're interested in. So I've packed this planner with the research assignments students and scientists have reported finding most useful over the years. They will allow you to evaluate what your future university values most, determine where your stories and goals intersect with its mission, and begin thinking about how you can leverage these things to elevate your application and essays. And, if it's earlier than the Spring semester of your junior year, you can even use this info to strategize your remaining time in high school towards this goal.

Endlessly customizable, the only rules are 1) make the book *work for you*, not the other way around, and 2) work in it a little bit every day. If a Control Panel prompt sparks an idea you like better, then do that - they *should be* doing so. If you spend the afternoon researching something tangentially-related, but important to you, that's a win! But while you should try to average about a half hour every day, to reach our 16-hour-total goal, you should know most days can be *technically* completed in 5 or 10 minutes. And what's more satisfying than a little malicious compliance on a rough day?

So if you've only got a few minutes today, that's okay. Just get started. Even if you only sit down and scribble, "blah, blah, blah, I'm getting into this school if it's the last thing I do!" all over the page, you still engaged with the goal today - and research shows that consistently doing that *just that alone* increases your chances of admission. So what are you waiting for? You literally can't lose.

This book consists of:

Your Dream School Profile: here you can jot down the cold hard facts that you'll want to avoid needing to look up over and over and over again - remember, inspiration favors the well-prepared!

SMART Goals and Priorities: use these worksheets and blank pages to plot out your goals and learn to chunk them into focused priorities that are sized perfectly for a to-do list.

Control Panel: holds your 30 daily goals/activities. Choose one to complete every day and mark it out when you're done. That's it. *PUBLISHER'S NOTE: Many of these have been specifically developed to be completed in novel/creative forms in order to best trigger the brain's centers of motivation, learning, and action. This is a feature, not a bug!*

Weekly Planner: this is where I want you to pour out all of your anxieties, procrastinations, and exciting plans. Yes, all these things MUST learn to get comfy-cozy with one another and figure out how to co-exist respectfully in one place - namely, your brain - because they've got a lot of years left to spend up there together.

Daily Journal: Five weeks' worth of two-page spreads where you can check in with your thoughts and feelings, complete a variety of short journaling prompts, write a paragraph or so in response to your daily control panel goal, read and reflect on an inspirational quote, and brainstorm possible next steps.

Dotted and lined pages: are for your notes, sketches, photos, and any other materials generated this month.

What's next? will give you clear, actionable steps you can take at any stage of the process, or once your work in this book is done.

Your Dream School
(a profile for those who want to be more than "just friends")

School Name and Nickname
_____

City, State, Region
_____

Rural, Urban, Suburban?
_____

Nearest Major City?
_____

Research University or Liberal Arts College?
_____

Public or Private?
_____

Student Body Population & Faculty Ratio
_____

Alumni Network?
_____

Avg admitted GPA & Test Scores
_____

Avg Acceptance Rates
_____

Rolling Admissions or Regular Decision Date
_____

Early Action/Early Decision Date?
_____

Test Blind or Optional?
_____

Graduation Rate?
_____

Job/Grad School Placement Rate?
_____

Your Dream School

(deets & data)

Annual Tuition & Fees

_____

Annual Room & Board

_____

Other Fees

_____

Other Expenses

_____

Travel Costs

_____

Insurance

_____

FAFSA Deadline

_____

Possible Scholarships

_____

Scholarship Deadline

_____

Institutional Financial Aid?

_____

Study Abroad Destinations

_____

Service Opportunities

_____

School Traditions

_____

School Mascot(s)

_____

School Colors

_____

Your Dream School

(anything's possible)

Possible Major #1

Possible Major #2

Possible Major #3

Possible Minor #1

Possible Minor #2

Possible Minor #3

Possible Greek Life

Possible Extracurricular #1

Possible Extracurricular #2

Possible Club #1

Possible Club #2

Possible Internships

Possible Research Opportunities

Possible Mentors

Possible On-Campus Jobs

Your Dream School

(marginalia)

daily goals control panel

RESEARCH

Has your dream school recently won any awards or accolades?

What is the school's culture? What are its stated mission and values? Why are you a good fit?

What were the essay prompts for your top school's application last year?

What course at your top school looks most interesting? Why?

What percentage of applicants got into your dream school last year?

WRITE

What was your childhood dream career? Why?

What would no one guess about your family just by looking?

How did you get involved in your favorite extracurricular?

Write about your favorite day in your least favorite class.

What will you escape, if you get into your dream school?

IMAGINE

How will going to college change your life?

How and where would you spend a gap year if money were no object?

Where will you study on campus? Be specific!

Who is your ideal roommate? What will you do with your actual roommate?

Where are you when you get the news that you've been accepted? Now what?

daily goals control panel

READ	DO	CREATE
A recent issue of your dream school's student paper.	Find three clubs you might be interested in joining and learn everything you can about them.	Draw a picture of your first day attending your dream school.
A paper or article by a professor in your intended major.	Watch an angry video posted online by a student at your dream school.	Write an acrostic poem with your dream school's abbreviated name.
A personal statement written by a student who was accepted into your dream school.	Write a thank you note to someone who's helped you get here.	Design a symbolic logo for your dream school.
What are the school's requirements for admission, remaining in good standing, and graduation?	Listen to a commencement speech for a past graduating class.	Rewrite the lyrics to a popular love song and sing it to your dream school.
The tips for getting into your dream school at admissionscontrol.com	Map out the journey from home to your top school. Will you return for holidays?	A collage merging photos of you, things special to you, and your top school.

SMART

GOALS

FOR SMART STUDENTS LIKE YOU!

CATEGORY	WHERE I'M CRUSHING IT	WHERE I'M FEELING CRUSHED	MY GOALS
COLLEGE PLANNING			
HEALTH			
FAMILY/ FRIENDS			
MENTAL HEALTH			
PERSONAL			
WORK/ SCHOOL			

SMART

PRIORITY SETTING

FOR SMART STUDENTS LIKE YOU!

S	<u>SPECIFIC</u> CONCISE AND CONCRETE?	Is this actually a task, or is it a goal, dream, desire, reaction, or amorphous ball of fear?
M	<u>MEASURABLE</u> SO I KNOW WHEN IT'S BEEN ACHIEVED?	Does it have a beginning, middle, and end point that I can verbalize & visualize?
A	<u>ACHIEVABLE</u> IN THE TIME FRAME AND WITH THE TOOLS I HAVE?	Is this possible yet? Are there other things that need to be done in preparation?
R	<u>RELEVANT</u> TO MY GOALS?	Will accomplishing this lead directly to a particular goal I have for my life?
T	<u>TO-DO</u> LIST FRIENDLY?	Is it focused enough to fit on my to-do list? If not, then how does it need to be modified?

01

WEEK ONE

01

WEEK ONE _____ **PRIORITIES**

TO-DO THIS WEEK:

- [ ] 7/7 daily goals complete
- [ ] 1/4 school profile complete
- [ ] Research school financing
- [ ] Follow the school on social media
- [ ] Bookmark all relevant websites
- [ ] _____
- [ ] _____
- [ ] _____
- [ ] _____

TO-DO THIS MONTH:

- [ ] Discuss: school financing w/family
- [ ] Strategize: application w/counselor
- [ ] Consider: what opportunities will be most important to you at university?
- [ ] _____
- [ ] _____

TO-DO THIS YEAR:

- [ ] Keep a running list of things you'd like schools to know about you
- [ ] Calculate time spent on all high school activities
- [ ] _____
- [ ] _____

PLANNER

	MORNING	AFTERNOON	NIGHT
MON			
TUE			
WED			
THU			
FRI			
SAT			
SUN			

Today I feel...

Yesterday I...

I recently learned...

> We are what we repeatedly do. Excellence, then, is not an act, but a habit.
>
> Aristotle

I'm proud of...

I'm grateful for the person who told me...

I'm anxious about...

In order to reach my goals I need...

I'll improve today by...

Date and Time: _____

Which daily goal was completed?

Possible next steps?

Today I feel...

Yesterday I...

I recently learned something that excited me...

To accomplish great things, we must not only act, but also dream; not only plan, but also believe.

Anatole France.

I'm proud of...

I'm grateful for...

Sometimes I'm still anxious about that time that I...

I need...

I'll improve today by...

Date and Time: _____

Which daily goal was completed?

Possible next steps?

Today I feel...

Yesterday I...

I recently learned...

If you are working on something
that you really care about, you
don't have to be pushed. The
vision pulls you.
Steve Jobs

I'm proud of...

I'm grateful for...

I'm anxious about...

Today I just need...

I'll improve today by...

Date and Time: _____

Which daily goal
was completed?

Possible next steps?

Today I feel...

Yesterday I...

I recently learned that if I...

It took me quite a long time to develop a voice, and now that I have it, I am not going to be silent.

Madeleine Albright

I'm proud of someone I know...

I'm grateful to my past self for...

I'm anxious about...

I need...

I'll improve today by telling someone what I need...

Date and Time: _____

Which daily goal was completed?

Possible next steps?

Today I feel...

Yesterday I...

I recently learned...

Education is the most powerful weapon which you can use to change the world.

Nelson Mandela

I'm proud that I was able to learn...

I'm grateful for...

I'm anxious about...

I still need to figure out...

I'll improve today by...

Date and Time: _____

Which daily goal
was completed?

Possible next steps?

Today I feel...

Yesterday I...

I recently learned...

I always wanted to be somebody, but now I realise I should have been more specific...

Lily Tomlin

I'm proud of the person I've become because...

I'm grateful to the people who've helped me get here...

I'm anxious about...

I need to tell someone that I forgot to...

I'll improve today by...

Date and Time: _____

Which daily goal
was completed?

Possible next steps?

Today I feel...

Yesterday I...

I'm glad that I learned the truth about...

Just one small positive thought in the morning can change your whole day.

Dalai Lama

I'm proud of...

I'm grateful for...

I'm anxious about...

I need to spend more time thinking about...

I'll improve today by...

Date and Time: _____

Which daily goal
was completed?

Possible next steps?

02

WEEK TWO

02

TO-DO THIS WEEK:

- [ ] 7/7 daily goals complete
- [ ] 2/4 school profile complete
- [ ] Find and follow a student who represents your school well online.
- [ ] _____
- [ ] _____
- [ ] _____
- [ ] _____
- [ ] _____

TO-DO THIS MONTH:

- [ ] Decide: will a school visit be possible?
- [ ] Update or create your resume.
- [ ] Learn everything you can about the school's city/state/area
- [ ] _____
- [ ] _____

TO-DO THIS YEAR:

- [ ] Rate all of your high school activities from most to least important to you
- [ ] Rate all of your high school activities from most to least impactful
- [ ] _____
- [ ] _____

PLANNER

	MORNING	AFTERNOON	NIGHT
MON			
TUE			
WED			
THU			
FRI			
SAT			
SUN			

Today I feel...

Yesterday I...

I recently learned this about myself...

You cannot plow a field by turning it over in your mind. To begin, begin.

Gordon B. Hinckley

I'm proud of...

I'm grateful for...

When I'm anxious I...

I need...

I'll improve my outlook on life today by...

Date and Time: _____

Which daily goal was completed?

Possible next steps?

Today I feel...

Yesterday I...

I recently learned this in my least favorite class...

One of the differences between some successful and unsuccessful people is that one group is full of doers, while the other is full of wishers.

Edmond Mbiaka

I'm proud of the time I successfully...

I'm grateful for...

I'm anxious about...

I need to treat myself...

I'll improve today by improving someone else's day...

Date and Time: _____

Which daily goal was completed?

Possible next steps?

Today I feel...

Yesterday I...

I recently learned this about a community I'm part of...

Don't settle for average. Bring your best to the moment. Then, whether it fails or succeeds, at least you know you gave all you had.
Angela Bassett

I'm proud of...

I'm grateful that I had the presence of mind to...

I'm anxious at the thought that I won't...

I need...

I'll improve today by...

Date and Time: _____

Which daily goal was completed?

Possible next steps?

Today I feel...

Yesterday I...

I recently learned...

The only one who can tell you "you can't win" is you, and you don't have to listen.

Jessica Ennis

I'm proud of...

I'm grateful to the teacher who...

I'm anxious about...

I need to spend more time...

I'll improve today by looking on the bright side of...

Date and Time: _____

Which daily goal
was completed?

Possible next steps?

Today I feel...

Yesterday I...

I recently learned...

Take your victories, whatever they may be, cherish them, use them, but don't settle for them.

Mia Hamm

I'm proud of the time I was victorious at...

I'm grateful for...

I'm anxious at the idea that I may never...

I need to find...

I'll improve today by...

Date and Time: _____

Which daily goal
was completed?

Possible next steps?

Today I feel...

Yesterday I...

I recently learned something really important outside of school...

I have never let my schooling interfere with my education.

Mark Twain

I'm proud of...

I'm grateful for...

I'm anxious about...

I need...

I'll improve today by spending a little time...

Date and Time: _____

Which daily goal
was completed?

Possible next steps?

Today I feel...

Yesterday I...

I recently imagined...

> Live out of your
> imagination, not your
> history.
>
> Stephen Covey

I'm proud of...

I'm grateful that I never...

I'm anxious about...

I need to be more open-minded about...

I'll improve today by...

Date and Time: _____

Which daily goal
was completed?

Possible next steps?

03

WEEK THREE

03

_____

TO-DO THIS WEEK:

- [ ] 7/7 daily goals complete
- [ ] 3/4 school profile complete
- [ ] Do something that brings you joy
- [ ] How will you get involved on campus? (What do you have to offer them?)
- [ ] _____
- [ ] _____
- [ ] _____
- [ ] _____

TO-DO THIS MONTH:

- [ ] Go back and add to prompts you might have rushed, when possible.
- [ ] Think: which teachers will write you the most enthusiastic letters of rec?
- [ ] _____
- [ ] _____

TO-DO THIS YEAR:

- [ ] Show teachers your collegiate side by speaking up in class, visiting office hours, and helping others.
- [ ] Research campus housing
- [ ] _____
- [ ] _____

PLANNER

	MORNING	AFTERNOON	NIGHT
MON			
TUE			
WED			
THU			
FRI			
SAT			
SUN			

Today I feel...

Yesterday I...

I recently learned that I want to...

If you really want to do something, you'll find a way. If you don't, you'll find an excuse.

Jim Rohn

I'm proud of...

I'm grateful for...

I'm anxious about...

I need to remember...

I'll improve today by finally crossing this off my to-do list...

Date and Time: _____

Which daily goal
was completed?

Possible next steps?

Today I feel...

Yesterday I...

I recently learned that if I really put my mind to it then I can...

The greater the difficulty, the more the glory in surmounting it.

Epicurus

I'm proud of...

I'm grateful for...

I'm anxious about going to university because...

To improve my health I need...

I'll improve today by looking around me...

Date and Time: _____

Which daily goal
was completed?

Possible next steps?

Today I feel...

Yesterday I...

I recently learned a tough lesson...

I will not lose, for even in defeat,
there's a valuable lesson learned.
So it evens up for me.

Jay-Z

I'm proud of...

I'm grateful that it all evened up when...

I get really anxious when I remember...

I need...

I'll improve today by...

Date and Time: _____

Which daily goal
was completed?

Possible next steps?

Today I feel...

Yesterday I...

I recently learned that I could push myself even harder when I...

If you don't risk anything, you risk even more.

Erica Jong

I'm proud of...

I'm grateful for...

I'm anxious about...

I need...

I'll improve today by taking a chance on...

Date and Time: _____

Which daily goal
was completed?

Possible next steps?

Today I feel...

Yesterday I...

I recently learned... ·

> Our greatest glory is not in never falling, but in rising every time we fall.
>
> Confucius

I'm proud that I always...

I'm grateful to my family for...

I'm anxious about...

In order to rise, I need...

I'll improve today by...

Date and Time: _____

Which daily goal
was completed?

Possible next steps?

Today I feel...

Yesterday I...

I recently changed my way of thinking about...

We cannot solve problems with the kind of thinking we employed when we came up with them..

Albert Einstein

I'm proud of the time I saw something everyone else missed...

I'm grateful for...

A problem I'm anxious about...

I need....

I'll improve today by reaching out to...

Date and Time: _____

Which daily goal was completed?

Possible next steps?

04

WEEK FOUR

04

TO-DO THIS WEEK:

- ☐ 7/7 daily goals complete
- ☐ Add all application dates - with weekly reminders - to your phone's calendar
- ☐ Something you've been putting off
- ☐ Think about majors of study
- ☐ _____
- ☐ _____
- ☐ _____
- ☐ _____

TO-DO THIS MONTH:

- ☐ Decide: is your resume as complete as it could be? What can you still add?
- ☐ Create memories with loved ones you'll cherish while away at school
- ☐ _____
- ☐ _____

TO-DO THIS YEAR:

- ☐ Focus on integrating your passion into other activities to increase intersections and complicate the narratives surrounding it.
- ☐ _____
- ☐ _____

PLANNER

	MORNING	AFTERNOON	NIGHT
MON			
TUE			
WED			
THU			
FRI			
SAT			
SUN			

Today I feel...

Yesterday I...

I recently learned that failure can...

Never let success get to your head and never let failure get to your heart.

Drake

I'm proud of...

I'm grateful for the fact that I can...

I get anxious about failing when...

I need...

I'll improve today by doing something I've been too afraid to do...

Date and Time: _____

Which daily goal
was completed?

Possible next steps?

Today I feel...

Yesterday I...

I recently learned...

Nothing ever goes away until it teaches us what we need to know.

Pema Chodron

I'm proud of...

I'm grateful that this thing kept bugging me until I realized what it was trying to teach me...

I'm anxious about...

I need...

I'll improve today by paying more attention to...

Date and Time: _____

Which daily goal
was completed?

Possible next steps?

Today I feel...

Yesterday I...

I recently learned...

First, forget inspiration. Habit is more dependable. Habit will sustain you whether you're inspired or not. Habit will help you finish and polish your stories.

Octavia Butler

I'm proud that I kept working when...

I'm grateful for that time I was inspired to...

Inspiration makes me anxious when...

I need...

I'll improve today by doing something without waiting for inspiration...

Date and Time: _____

Which daily goal
was completed?

Possible next steps?

Today I feel...

Yesterday I...

I recently realized all of the progress I've made in...

If there is no struggle, there is no progress.

Frederick Douglass

I'm proud of...

I'm grateful for this struggle because...

I'm anxious about...

In order to get over a current struggle I need...

I'll improve today by...

Date and Time: _____

Which daily goal
was completed?

Possible next steps?

Today I feel...

Yesterday I...

I recently learned...

Keep a little fire burning;
however small, however hidden.

Cormac McCarthy

I'm proud of...

I'm grateful for this person who stoked my internal fires...

I'm anxious about...

I need...

I'll improve today by warming my hands at a friend's "little fire" and telling them how proud I am of them...

Date and Time: _____

Which daily goal
was completed?

Possible next steps?

Today I feel...

Yesterday I...

I recently learned that I'm strong enough to...

Courage is like a muscle. We strengthen it by use.

Ruth Gordon

I'm proud of the time I found the courage to...

I'm grateful for...

I'm anxious about...

I need...

I'll improve today by...

Date and Time: _____

Which daily goal was completed?

Possible next steps?

Today I feel...

Yesterday I...

I recently learned that my family...

If it makes you nervous, you're doing it right.

Childish Gambino

I'm proud of...

I'm grateful to the author who...

I'm anxious about...

I need to face my fears about...

I'll improve today by...

Date and Time: _____

Which daily goal
was completed?

Possible next steps?

WEEK FIVE

TO-DO THIS WEEK:

- ☐ Last 2 daily goals complete
- ☐ 4/4 school profile complete
- ☐ Create: your own final daily goals
- ☐ List: what do you still need to research, look up, or do?
- ☐ Reflect: why is this school unique?
- ☐ Reflect: why is it your perfect fit?
- ☐ _____
- ☐ _____

TO-DO THIS MONTH:

- ☐ Don't worry too much about things you can't control - it only wastes time you could spend on things you CAN change!
- ☐ _____
- ☐ _____

TO-DO THIS YEAR:

- ☐ Find someone you trust to help you brainstorm and edit essays
- ☐ Read all you can about applying
- ☐ _____
- ☐ _____
- ☐ _____

PLANNER

	MORNING	AFTERNOON	NIGHT
MON			
TUE			
WED			
THU			
FRI			
SAT			
SUN			

Today I feel...

Yesterday I...

I recently learned that my school...

A surplus of effort could overcome a deficit of confidence.

Sonia Sotomayor

I'm proud of...

I'm grateful for...

I'm anxious about...

In order to feel more confident I need...

I'll improve today by making an effort to...

Date and Time: _____

Which daily goal
was completed?

Possible next steps?

Today I feel...

Yesterday I...

I recently learned something about the world...

And the day came when the risk to remain tight in a bud was more painful than the risk it took to blossom.
Anais Nin

I'm proud that I took the risk of

I'm grateful for the person who invented...

I'm anxious about...

I need...

I'll improve today by...

Date and Time: _____

Which daily goal
was completed?

Possible next steps?

Today I feel...

Yesterday I...

I recently learned that I'm unprepared for...

Education is the passport to the future, for tomorrow belongs to those who prepare for it today.

Malcolm X

I'm proud of...

I'm grateful that I didn't give up on learning...

I'm anxious about...

I need to learn more about...

I'll improve today by studying for...

Date and Time: _____

Which daily goal
was completed?

Possible next steps?

Today I feel...

Yesterday I...

I recently learned that I'm capable of giving...

You receive from the world what you give to the world.

Oprah Winfrey

I'm proud of...

I'm grateful that the world has given me...

I'm anxious about...

I need...

I'll improve today by paying something forward...

Date and Time: _____

Which daily goal
was completed?

Possible next steps?

Today I feel...

Yesterday I...

I recently learned that I care more about something than I thought...

You lose nothing when fighting for a cause... In my mind the losers are those who don't have a cause they care about.
Muhammad Ali

I'm proud of...

I'm grateful for people who...

I'm anxious that it might be too late to do anything about...

In order to make a difference I need...

I'll improve today by...

Date and Time: _____

Which daily goal
was completed?

Possible next steps?

Today I feel...

Yesterday I...

I recently learned...

Failure is the opportunity to begin again more intelligently.

Henry Ford

I'm proud of the time I realized I could...

I'm grateful I got the second chance to...

I'm anxious about failing because...

I need to quit wishing...

I'll improve today by showing forgiveness...

Date and Time: _____

Which daily goal was completed?

Possible next steps?

Today I feel...

Yesterday I...

I recently learned something about history...

Your story is what you have, what you will always have. It is something to own.

Michelle Obama

I'm proud of...

I'm grateful for...

I'm anxious about owning this part of my story...

I need...

I'll improve today by giving a story a new and improved ending...

Date and Time: _____

Which daily goal was completed?

Possible next steps?

What Next?

(???)

Congratulations! You're (at least) another month older than you were when you received this book. How's it feel?

I truly hope it feels great to know that you're *exponentially* closer to reaching your university goals. You've greatly improved your chances of getting into one of your dream schools just by being proactive about educating yourself and reflecting on the intersections between this university's mission, values, and vision and your own personality traits, skills, experiences, and goals.

You've also - whether you realized it or not - been priming the pump to the well of your creativity. The reflections you'll need to draw from in order to complete your college essays *require* this. Just remember: the deeper the well the cleaner the water; similarly, the first thoughts drawn forth from our minds aren't always the best we have to give. Sometimes the answers to these prompts can be most useful in simply showing us where to start digging, with the intention of clearing dross and going just a little deeper each time.

If you've enjoyed our time together and want to know if you might be a good fit for live consulting, group workshops, or my asynchronous app-based courses go to www.admissionscontrol.com/readers for a special offer! You can also check out information on my other books and the many free resources posted there.

You might also consider:

Asking your school counselor if they can get you in contact with a former student from your high school who successfully applied to your dream university and might be willing to let you pick their brain for essay ideas, share a copy of their winning application, or crash on their dorm floor for a weekend visit.

Using the strategies you learned this month to research the rest of the schools on your list. You don't need to put a full 16 hours into each of them since you'll be able to navigate the websites and understand the information you're taking in more quickly the second time around. *Pro-tip: pay special attention to your safety schools, if you do end up at one of them you want to have done everything you can to ensure that you stand a good chance of being happy there.*

Reaching out to an experienced educational consultant or college advisor for a review of your application, essays, admissions strategy, or school list. During interviews or initial consultations be sure you get a good sense of the breadth and depth of their experience, ask for sample essays, and figure out what would be expected of all parties. Feel out their organizational and communication skills. Do they seem to be winging it, or do they have a system in place? How will you communicate and handle passing drafts back and forth for review? What will you do during live sessions or workshops? Don't be afraid to ask questions! You'll have many in the coming months and won't want to work with someone who gets annoyed at having to answer them.

You might also consider:

Transcribing your answers from this journal into a digital notebook that's syncable to all your devices so you'll be able to easily search and scan for patterns and connections when working on your essays and other parts of your applications. (For more on this see my book, *How Smart Students Get into Their Dream Schools: Ten Things You MUST do Before Submitting the Common App.*)

Creating a dedicated space (if you don't utilize a digital notebook) to save your thoughts, links, and other important information while researching and on the go. You never know when the perfect opening line will pop into your head, the perfect sample essay will come across your screen just as you're rushing out the door, or you'll overhear the perfect piece of inspirational advice while sitting in a coffee shop with friends. Ensure that you can embed photos, screenshots, and voice memos into your notes, at the very least.

Going back through the Control Panel and completing any prompts that you resisted or rushed the first time around. The prompts I see students gaining the biggest advantages from tend to be those they immediately fall in love with and those they immediately hate. The reason? There's generally something in those you want to resist that makes you feel a little vulnerable, and when we can get past the discomfort and allow ourselves to lean into it we often write our strongest, most authentic essays. Protip: If you're reading this and feeling a little offended, thinking, "no, actually, the prompt is just really freaking stupid..." then that's a pretty good sign you're putting up a wall. We simply don't get that emotionally worked up about the meaningless things in life, do we?

You might also consider:

Completing the following brainstorming prompts that I use to get my students ready for writing their college essays. **We generally begin these during spring in their junior year and continue adding to them until early fall in their senior year.**

How would your best friend describe you? What about your guardian?

How would you describe the ten most important people in your life? Be thorough!

How does your gender and/or sexuality define you or influence your life, if at all?

Who motivates or influences you the most? Do they know this? If not, why?

Name ten problems or challenges you've faced. How did you solve or overcome them?

What inspires you? Why? What do you do about it? What do you wish you could do?

Name ten things that make you happy. Which makes you happiest? Why?

What do you enjoy least about your extracurriculars? What have you dropped? Why?

What do you need, in order to successfully reach your goals in life?

Name ten of your weaknesses or shortcomings. How do you make up for them?

What is one thing you hope your interviewers WON"T ask. Why?

What would you do with the rest of your life if you didn't have to worry about money?

Name ten things you've failed at. Which one still stings the most. Why?

Name ten communities you belong to. What makes them special?

If you had a time machine where and when would you visit first? Why?

Exclusive Reader Resources

As an exclusive gift to our readers, we have created a top-secret web page where you can instantly:

- Download additional resources

- Find links to recommended programs and software

- Access special offers and promotional codes

- Take your next steps in the journey to reaching your educational goals!

This page is updated regularly, so be sure to check it out often!

www.admissionscontrol/readers

TYPE SET GROW

words to live by

Made in the USA
Middletown, DE
16 February 2023

25017651R00084

About the Author

Johnathan Patin-Sauls is a former English and psychology instructor who currently works as an editor and educational consultant. He combines his knowledge of human nature, neuroscience, and storytelling to help students find, tell, and cultivate their most engaging stories.

You can email him at jake@admissionscontrol.com

One Request

Thanks so much for taking this journey with me! I'm positive that if you completed all the suggestions presented here you'll be well on your way to becoming a student at one of your chosen universities.

When you do, I'd love to hear from you! If you're interested in being interviewed for a future book, sharing your winning essays as successful samples to help future students, or working together in some other way, please let me know.

But before you go, I also have a small, quick favor to ask. Would you mind taking a minute or two and leaving an honest review of this journal on Amazon? Reviews are the BEST way to help others decide to purchase this book, and I also check them for helpful feedback when creating new editions.

To find out how to do this visit:

admissionscontrol.com/tmrds

If you have any questions, think you might like to work with me one-on-one, or would just like to tell me directly what you thought of the journal, shoot me an email at jake@admissionscontrol.com. I'd love to hear from you!